Table of Contents

RSL 11+ Comprehension: Volume 2

Getting the most out of this pack

These papers are structured like those in the original RSL 11+ Comprehension, offering students further practice with the same types of exam. Type A here matches Type A there, and so on. They are in general pitched at a *slightly* harder level: the passages are on average longer, and the hardest paper (8) here is a little more difficult than paper 8 in the first pack.

The solution pages not only mark, but thoroughly teach the lessons from each exercise (these are things that I say frequently to my pupils). Some students will be able to use them independently, but they have been created with a supportive adult in mind: this pack will allow a parent to step confidently into the role of tutor.

Please bear in mind that the example solutions are *no more than suggestions*. Very few of them claim to be the only possible approach. Read the discussion around each one if you want advice for assessing a different answer.

Although these papers have been designed carefully in response to the exams set by many schools in recent years, they cannot attempt to imitate every design of test, and they are not predictive. Sometimes a school sets another sort of exam: for example, a multiple choice test. However, the skills of reading and analysis addressed in this pack will be a valuable preparation for any type of comprehension.

How to use this pack

These materials can be used in different ways. For example, you may wish to answer some papers while reading the solutions, in order to understand how a comprehension exam works. However, most people will choose to write their answers then refer to the marking sheet.

When you are correcting your work, it is a good idea to take notes of any important points: this will help you to remember them. Also, if your answer could be improved, it is often worth re-writing it with reference to the mark scheme.

These papers will be most useful if you complete them in order. Although each test and mark sheet can stand alone, used in sequence they will build up your skills steadily. There are eight papers, two of each type. The first of each pair provides answer spaces, while for the second you should use writing paper: this way you will learn to judge the best length for your answers.

These papers have been designed for use without a time limit, because they are focused on teaching each student to produce skilful, carefully written answers. When these skills have been acquired, it is usually a fairly simple matter to speed them up with the past papers available from most schools. Timing problems are almost always caused by a lack of confidence with core techniques.

P.T.O.

Essential advice for comprehension tests

- Read the passage; underline anything you do not fully understand.
- Read the questions.
- Re-read the passage, working out your underlined phrases as best you can, now that you know the full context.
- Underline the key words in each question as you come to it (e.g. 'why', 'own words', 'evidence', 'lines 20-23').
- Look at the number of marks available for the question, and work out how your answer should be structured.
- Read the necessary paragraphs and underline any useful evidence. Keep underlining/quotations short, if possible (no more than six words).
- After writing your answer, check that you have answered every part of the question and have written enough for the number of marks.
- Proof-read your English.
- Move on to the next question.

Never leave a blank space! If all else fails, make an educated guess. You might still get marks.

Finally, never cross out an answer unless you have already *completed* an improved one.

Also Available

GCSE Maths by RSL, Higher Level (9-1), Non-Calculator: Volume 1
GCSE Spanish by RSL
RSL 11+ Comprehension: Volume 1
RSL 11+ Maths: Volume 1
RSL 8+ Comprehension
RSL 13+ Comprehension

Coming soon

RSL 11+ Maths: Volume 2
GCSE English by RSL
A Level Maths by RSL (books for each module)

We are a young business in a competitive marketplace. We want to improve and expand our range, providing even better products for our customers, including families who may not wish to purchase long courses of private tuition. If you have any feedback, please let us know! Our email address is rsleducational@gmail.com.

If you like this product, please tell your friends and write a review on Amazon!

RSL 11+ Comprehension: Volume 2
By Robert lomax
Published by RSL Educational
Copyright © Robert Lomax 2016

The Shepherd's Life (paper 1 – type A)

James Rebanks is a sheep farmer from Matterdale, in the Lake District.

The alarm clock vibrates on the bedside table. My hand swipes across and kills it: 4.30 a.m. I was only half-asleep anyway. The room is already half-lit with the coming dawn. I see my wife's shoulder, and her leg curled over the sheet, and my two-year-old son lying between us, where he came in during the night. I move quietly out of the room with a fistful of clothes.
5   The sun will rise soon over the edge of the fell.

In the kitchen I swig at a carton of milk. I throw on my clothes robotically, half-awake. I have half an hour before we are meeting at the fell gate. We are going to gather the fell flock in for clipping (shearing). My mind is on a kind of checklist autopilot.

          Right clothes: check.
10   Breakfast: check.
          Sandwiches: check.
          Boots: check.

As I get to the barn, my sheepdogs Floss and Tan jump, wriggle and make whining noises until I unchain them. They know we are going to the fell. I feed them so they'll have energy
15   later when they need it. A shepherd on a fell without a good sheepdog, or dogs, is useless. The fell sheep are half-wild, can smell weakness, and would escape and create chaos without good sheepdogs. Men can't get to lots of places the dogs can – to the crags and rocky screes, to chase the ewes down. When I head out, Tan bolts for the barn door and jumps on the quad bike. Floss follows.

20   Sheepdogs fed and loaded: check.
          Quad bike: check.
          Fuel: check.

The swallows explode outwards from the barn door, disturbed by the dogs. They fledged a couple of days ago and whole families head out over my head to the fields where they hawk
25   all day over the grass and thistles.

Fingers of pink and orange light are now creeping over the fell sides. Sunrise.

From *The Shepherd's Life*, by James Rebanks, pages 6-7. Reproduced by permission of Penguin Books Ltd. Published London 2015; copyright © James Rebanks 2015.

1.   Write down a word that means the same as 'vibrates'.   **(1)**

....

2.   Why does the shepherd take 'a fistful of clothes' out of the room?   **(2)**

....

....

3.   What does 'I throw on my clothes robotically' mean?   **(3)**

....

....

....

....

....

4.   Sometimes the atmosphere of the passage is calm; sometimes it is more exciting.

          (a) Write down a brief example of each of these moods.   **(2)**

Calm: ....

....

Exciting: ....

....

          (b) What does this contrast suggest to you about how the shepherd feels?   **(3)**

....

....

....

....

....

5.   The word 'fell' is used several times. What do you think it means here?   **(2)**

....

6.   What effects do you think the writer is aiming for in lines 9-12 and 20-22?   (3)

....

....

....

....

....

....

7.   'A shepherd on a fell without a good sheepdog ... is useless' (line 15). Explain in
      your own words why this is the case.   (4)

....

....

....

....

....

....

8.   How does the author make the final paragraph effective?   (5)

....

....

....

....

....

....

....

....

[TOTAL 25]

The Shepherd's Life – Solutions

1.   Write down a word that means the same as 'vibrates'.   (1)

> shakes

'Shakes', 'wobbles', 'jiggles','buzzes', 'trembles', or anything that conveys a similar meaning is fine.

- 'Write down' means that you do not need to answer with a full sentence.

An answer such as 'shaking' or 'shook' might lose half a mark: you need to <u>write in the same tense as 'vibrates'</u>.

2.   Why does the shepherd take 'a fistful of clothes' out of the room?   (2)

> He does this so that he can get dressed in a different room, where he will not wake up his wife and son.

The main point is that he does not want to disturb his family. To be certain of two marks, the answer also needs to say, or at least imply, that he will get dressed elsewhere.

Questions like this should be answered <u>in full sentences</u>, but this doesn't mean that you need to repeat the question in your answer.

3.   What does 'I throw on my clothes robotically' mean?   (3)

> 'Throw on' suggests that the shepherd dresses quickly, without worrying about how he looks. 'Robotically' means that he is not really thinking about it – he is just doing what he always does, maybe because he is tired.

To get full marks, the answer needs to explain

- 'throw on'; and
- 'robotically'.

<u>An explanation of only one could achieve a maximum of two marks.</u>

When you have to explain a quotation, you should <u>underline the important words</u> before you begin ('throw on' and 'robotically' in this case). Your answer needs to explain all of them.

Note that the example answer briefly makes two extra points ('he is just doing what he always does' and 'he is tired'), so that it will get full marks even if the marker is in a bad mood.

4.   **Sometimes the atmosphere of the passage is calm; sometimes it is more exciting.**

(a) Write down a brief example of each of these moods.   **(2)**

Calm:	'I see my wife's shoulder, and her leg curled over the sheet'
Exciting:	'swallows explode outwards'

For a question like this, it is a good idea to <u>underline several possibilities, then choose the best ones</u>.

(b) What does this contrast suggest to you about how the shepherd feels?   **(3)**

> The shepherd is still feeling tired: his thoughts are drowsy. He also feels peaceful because everybody else is asleep and he has the world to himself. However, there are times when the energy of the natural world makes him excited by the new day, even though he is sleepy.

Your answer needs to deal with the word 'contrast'. Ideally you should explain <u>what we learn from the *difference*</u> between the two moods. The last sentence of the example does this because it <u>links the shepherd's different emotions</u> ('excited … even though he is sleepy').

However, any answer which <u>clearly explains the two feelings</u> – calmness and excitement – might well get full marks.

5.   **The word 'fell' is used several times. What do you think it means here?**   **(2)**

> 'Fell' means 'hill'.

Any similar word, like 'mountain', would also be fine for two marks.

You don't need to guess. If you don't know a word, <u>find all the places where it is used, and hunt for clues</u>. For example, the dawn will come 'over the edge of the fell'.

An answer that recognises a fell as <u>part of the landscape</u> (e.g. 'A fell is a field on the shepherd's farm') would be worth one mark.

This is an example of a two-mark question which only requires one point. There are two marks for an accurate response, while one mark is available for partial understanding. Remember that <u>there is nothing wrong with making a second point</u> if you are unsure whether it is needed. For example, 'A fell is a hill in parts of northern England'.

6.   **What effects do you think the writer is aiming for in lines 9-12 and 20-22?**   **(3)**

> This list repeats the word 'check', which makes it sound as though the shepherd is preparing for something important and maybe risky, like a pilot getting ready to take off. Also, because it is so simple ('breakfast … fuel') and repetitive, you can clearly imagine him running through the list in his head.

There are two important things here:

- Because the word 'effect<u>s</u>' is plural and the question is worth several marks, the answer <u>needs to make more than one point</u>. Two points should be enough.
- 'Effects' means that you should explain <u>the ideas and feelings the list creates in the reader's mind</u> ('makes it sound as though'; 'you can clearly imagine').

7.   **'A shepherd on a fell without a good sheepdog … is useless' (line 15). Explain in your own words why this is the case.**   **(4)**

> The hill sheep won't follow instructions, and they can tell if a shepherd and his dogs aren't good enough to control them. If they do get out of control, they will run off and make trouble. Finally, there are lots of places a skilled dog can reach that a human can't.

To get four marks safely, you should aim to find <u>four different points in the passage</u> and <u>re-write them in your own words</u>.

There are four or five possibilities, and the example above contains all of them. The original quotations are these:

- 'half-wild'
- 'can smell weakness'
- 'escape'
- 'create chaos'
- 'men can't get to lots of places the dogs can'

You should find and underline these in the passage before you write your answer.

Writing in your own words means <u>not using important words from the text</u>: you change the words *to show that you understand their meaning*. However, there is nothing wrong with repeating common words which are difficult to avoid, like 'can't', 'won't', 'dog' and 'shepherd'.

Each correct point made *not* in your own words would probably be worth half a mark. For example, 'they can make chaos' would be too close to the original wording, 'create chaos': you need to put the idea of 'chaos' into your own words to show that you understand it.

8.   **How does the author make the final paragraph effective?**   (5)

> The author describes the rays of light as 'fingers'. This metaphor makes me imagine the early dawn as dots of light peeping over the rim of the hills ('fell sides'). When they 'creep over', the rest of the hand seems to come into view, as the points of light join together and make the sky bright. The one-word sentence, 'Sunrise', is surprising. It suggests that the shepherd is amazed by the new day, or at least very happy to see it.

Try to find <u>at least two things</u> to discuss. If you can name them ('metaphor'; 'short sentence'), this is good, but don't worry if you can't.

The main thing is to focus on 'how' (so think about the writer's methods) and 'effective' (which means that you have to think about <u>the *effect* of the words on a reader's thoughts or feelings</u>).

You should give the marker <u>five different things to tick</u>. In the example, the first point (about the 'fingers' of light) would comfortably be worth three marks, and the second (about the one-word sentence) would be worth two or three, so the answer clearly achieves five marks overall.

A Troupe of Trained Tops – solutions

1.   Where is this story set?   **(2)**

> It is set in Saint Mark's Square, Venice.

Or

> It is set in Venice, by the Doge's Palace.

You need to notice (from the offer of two marks) that this requires <u>more than just 'Venice'</u>. The marks are for:

- correctly naming the city;
- an accurate extra detail.

You will not get a mark for 'Europe', as this information is given to you above the passage.

2.   Using your own words as far as possible, describe the early afternoon behaviour of the crabs and pigeons in lines 1-10.   **(4)**

> The crabs, stranded by the low tide, hang on sleepily to the walls in places where the stones are still damp. The pigeons also rest, high up on the walls of the grand buildings, their heads covered by their wings.

The slight trick in this question is that lines 4-7 are irrelevant: this paragraph describes how the pigeons behave at *other* times of day. You would be unlikely to *lose* marks for mentioning how they fly down when tempted by grain, but <u>you have to include the information from paragraph 3, about how they sleep in the early afternoon</u>.

<u>'Using your own words'</u> is the important phrase here. It is always wise to underline such things before you write. Notice how phrases have been adapted <u>to show understanding</u>:

- For example, 'clinging lazily to the stone walls of the houses, wherever there was a place still cool and wet' has become 'hang on sleepily to the walls in places where the stones are still damp.'

In this case, notice how words such as 'wall', 'stone' and 'place' have survived. You need to change the language *enough to show that you understand what is going on*, but you can keep those common words which could only be replaced by writing very strangely.

3.   **Edith and her mother show very different attitudes to the city in lines 16-35. Giving evidence to support your points, explain what these attitudes suggest about their personalities.**   **(4)**

> Edith is so intrigued by Venice that she 'should like to get lost' there. She is a very curious person, fascinated by 'beautiful old' things. Her mother prefers things that are 'safe': she finds Venice threatening. She is an unadventurous person who likes to view a city 'from a hotel window'.

This looks like a difficult question: it is wordy ('different attitudes to the city'; 'what these attitudes suggest about their personalities') and mixes ideas together (the characters' attitudes to Venice and their personalities).

However, if you <u>think about the number of marks available</u>, it is possible to come up with a simple and effective structure:

- Edith's attitude: 1 mark
- Edith's personality: 1 mark
- Her mother's attitude: 1 mark
- Her mother's personality: 1 mark

Try to keep your points about personality distinct from your points about attitude. Notice how the example does this by using several sentences.

Finally, it is important that <u>your answer should include quotations</u>. One quote for each character will be fine. Unquoted references to the passage can also be acceptable as evidence, but it is always more convincing to quote directly.

- <u>Keep your quotes short</u> – a maximum of four or five words, if possible.

4.   **Using your own words, describe how the**

   (a) Japanese;
   (b) German; and
   (c) English

   tops spin.   **(6)**

There are <u>two marks available for each part</u> of this question.

> **(a)** The Japanese tops spin delicately, moving quickly around, but do not last long.

There are three concepts in lines 48-49 ('light', 'agile' and 'spin only a moment'). You should <u>aim to include all three, but two are *likely* to be adequate</u>.

> **(b)** The German tops are very noisy, and spin clumsily.

Based on 'great humming sound' and 'not at all graceful'.

> **(c)** The English tops spin well but not beautifully, before slipping sideways and toppling over.

You need to show some understanding of 'solid, business-like … that do their work', and 'go off at the close … with a bow and an off-hand dash'.

5.   **Why do you think Edith trusts Rafael? Give evidence from the text to support your opinions.**   **(6)**

> Rafael seems friendly, because he looks right 'into her face' and he 'smiles'. Also, the other boys seem to like him, because they 'laugh' when he talks to them. He is 'dressed with care', which suggests that he is sensible and well-organised.

Be careful not to use evidence from lines 57-58: at this point Rafael is talking in Italian, which Edith does not understand.

You need <u>three reasons, with evidence for each</u>. It is possible that two very well-explained points, with evidence, might get six marks, but you should not rely on this.

Any reasonable points should get marks. Other possibilities might include:

* He has good manners (he 'takes off his cap').
* He is clever and well-organised, because he skilfully present his spinning-top collection to tourists in the square. (This is similar to the final point in the example, so you could not use both.)

You *might* get marks for referring to Rafael's good English, but it is debatable how much this has to do with *trust*.

Notice how the example takes some quotations in the past tense and changes them into the present (for instance, 'smiled' [line 61] has become 'smiles') so as to fit in with the rest of the answer. This is acceptable – in fact, it makes for good English – but it isn't something to worry about very much at 11+.

6.   **Imagine that Edith's mother replies to Rafael's offer in lines 65-66. Write what she says.**   **(3)**

You could decide that she does not like Rafael:

> 'And why should we trust you to show them to us, young man? We are perfectly capable of observing this fine city, in our own way, without putting our lives in the hands of young men who spin tops pointlessly in public spaces!'

Alternatively, you could imagine that she has been charmed by him:

> 'My daughter and I wish to be shown the sights of Venice safely, without being tipped into any canals. Can you manage that? Yes, I suppose you probably can. After all, your manners are quite decent. But do please leave those accursed tops behind.'

This is a creative writing question, but also a piece of comprehension: Edith's mother needs to speak in a way that makes sense, based on her character in the rest of the passage.

Because it is a creative question, you are liable to lose a mark or two if you make many mistakes.

As there are only three marks, your answer does not need to be particularly long.

The Thirty-Nine Steps (paper 3 – type B)

The story is set in Scotland, just before the start of the First World War. Richard Hannay is lying on top of a dovecot (a house for doves), hiding from German spies who want to kill him.

I woke with a burning head and the sun glaring in my face. For a long time I lay motionless, for those horrible fumes seemed to have loosened my joints and dulled my brain. Sounds came to me from the house – men speaking throatily and the throbbing of a stationary car. There was a little gap in the parapet to which I wriggled, and from which I had some sort of

5   view of the yard. I saw figures come out – a servant with his head bound up, and then a younger man in knickerbockers*. They were looking for something, and moved towards the mill. Then one of them caught sight of the wisp of cloth on the nail, and cried out to the other. They both went back to the house, and brought two more to look at it. I saw the rotund figure of my late captor, and I thought I made out the man with the lisp. I noticed that all had

10   pistols.

For half an hour they ransacked the mill. I could hear them kicking over the barrels and pulling up the rotten planking. Then they came outside, and stood just below the dovecot arguing fiercely. I heard them fiddling with the door of the dovecot and for one horrid moment I fancied they were coming up. Then they thought better of it, and went back to the

15   house.

All that long blistering afternoon I lay baking on the rooftop. Thirst was my chief torment. My tongue was like a stick, and to make it worse I could hear the cool drip of water from the mill-lade*. I watched the course of the little stream as it came in from the moor, and my fancy followed it to the top of the glen, where it must issue from an icy fountain fringed with

20   cool ferns and mosses. I would have given a thousand pounds to plunge my face into that.

I had a fine prospect of the whole ring of moorland. I saw the car speed away with two occupants, and a man on a hill pony riding east. I judged they were looking for me, and I wished them joy of their quest.

But I saw something else more interesting. The house stood almost on the summit of a swell

25   of moorland which crowned a sort of plateau, and there was no higher point nearer than the big hills six miles off. The actual summit, as I have mentioned, was a biggish clump of trees – firs mostly, with a few ashes and beeches. On the dovecot I was almost on a level with the tree-tops, and could see what lay beyond. The wood was not solid, but only a ring, and inside was an oval of green turf, for all the world like a big cricket-field.

30   I didn't take long to guess what it was. It was an aerodrome, and a secret one. The place had been most cunningly chosen. For suppose anyone were watching an aeroplane descending here, he would think it had gone over the hill beyond the trees. As the place was on the top of a rise in the midst of a big amphitheatre, any observer from any direction would conclude it had passed out of view behind the hill. Only a man very close at hand would realize that the

35   aeroplane had not gone over but had descended in the midst of the wood. An observer with a telescope on one of the higher hills might have discovered the truth, but only herds went there, and herds do not carry spy-glasses. When I looked from the dovecot I could see far

away a blue line which I knew was the sea, and I grew furious to think that our enemies had this secret conning-tower to rake our waterways.

40 Then I reflected that if that aeroplane came back the chances were ten to one that I would be discovered. So through the afternoon I lay and prayed for the coming of darkness, and glad I was when the sun went down over the big western hills and the twilight haze crept over the moor. The aeroplane was late. The gloaming was far advanced when I heard the beat of wings and saw it gliding downward to its home in the wood. Lights twinkled for a bit and
45 there was much coming and going from the house. Then the dark fell, and silence.

Adapted from *The Thirty-Nine Steps* by John Buchan

knickerbockers: baggy trousers ending just below the knee
mill-lade: the channel which drives a water-wheel (also 'mill race')

1.   **Why does one of the men 'cry out' when he sees 'the wisp of cloth on the nail' (line 7)?**   **(2)**

....

....

....

2.   **Give the meanings of the following words, as they are used in the passage:**

(a) ransacked (line 11)   .... **(1)**

(b) herd (line 36)   .... **(1)**

3.   **Explain the effect of the alliteration (repeated consonant sounds) in each of the following quotations:**

(a) 'All that long blistering afternoon I lay baking on the rooftop.' (line 16)   **(2)**

....

....

....

(b) 'an icy fountain fringed with cool ferns and mosses' (lines 19-20)   **(2)**

....

....

....

4.   **Using your own words as far as possible, describe the location of the house. Base your answer on lines 24-27.**   **(3)**

....

....

....

....

....

5.   **Explain fully why the location of the aerodrome is 'cunningly chosen' (line 31).**

                                                                                       (4)

....

....

....

....

....

....

6.   **Why does Hannay 'pray for the coming of darkness' (line 41)?**   **(2)**

....

....

....

7.   **The author uses the same technique when describing the sun in line 1 and the 'twilight haze' in line 42.**

      (a) What is the name of this technique?   ....   **(2)**

      (b) Explain why the example in line 42 is effective.   **(3)**

....

....

....

....

....

8.   **What are your impressions of Richard Hannay's character (personality)? Give evidence to support your points.   (6)**

....

....

....

....

....

....

....

....

9.   **How are the last three sentences made particularly effective?   (6)**

....

....

....

....

....

....

....

....

....

....

[TOTAL 34]

The Thirty-Nine Steps – solutions

1.   **Why does one of the men 'cry out' when he sees 'the wisp of cloth on the nail'
        (line 7)?**   **(2)**

> He is excited because he thinks they are about to find Hannay, whose clothes the
> 'wisp of cloth' has probably come from.

For two marks, you need to include an explanation of *why this cloth suggests that Richard
Hannay is nearby.*

2.   **Give the meanings of the following words, as they are used in the passage:**

        (a) ransacked (line 11)   **(1)**

> searched thoroughly

Something to do with making a terrible mess might also be acceptable here.

        (b) herd (line 36)   **(1)**

> somebody who looks after farm animals

'Shepherd' ought to be okay.

The limited answer space should make it clear to you that full sentences are not required here.

3.   **Explain the effect of the alliteration (repeated consonant sounds) in each of the
        following quotations:**

        (a) 'All that long blistering afternoon I lay baking on the rooftop.' (line 16)   (2)

> The 'l' sounds suggest the lazy stillness of the afternoon, while the repeated 'b' is like
> the sun beating Hannay painfully.

You probably don't need to notice that the 'l' *and* 'b' sounds repeat: <u>if you made two points
about one of them, this should be fine</u>.

When writing about the way words sound, ask yourself these questions:

- Do the words sound like a thing which is happening in the passage?
- Does the sound of the words create an emotion?

In this case, the answer to the first question might be 'no' or 'only sort of', but the second
question opens up some useful possibilities.

(b) 'an icy fountain fringed with cool ferns and mosses' (lines 19-20)   (2)

> The 'f' is like the cold breeze rustling the ferns, in Hannay's imagination. It is calm, like the place he longs for.

The first sentence might be enough here, but the second makes sure.

4.   **Using your own words as far as possible, describe the location of the house. Base your answer on lines 24-27.   (3)**

> It is just below a fairly large wood which tops a rounded hill. This hill rises from a high, flat area of moor. It is the highest place for six miles.

Your answer <u>must include</u> the following ideas:

- 'almost on the summit'
- ... 'of a swell of moorland'
- 'the actual summit ... was a ... clump of trees'

Some markers would expect the following points, but it is only a three mark question so you ought to survive without them:

- 'which crowned a sort of plateau'
- 'no higher point nearer than ... six miles off'

Notice how the example includes all these ideas. Some words ('moor' and 'six miles', for instance) are difficult to rephrase and can be left as they are.

5.   **Explain fully why the location of the aerodrome is 'cunningly chosen' (line 31).**
                                                                                    (4)

> It is at the highest point for a long way, so nobody can easily look down onto it, and the trees mean that you cannot see the runway. Therefore, anybody watching a plane coming in to land would imagine that it had flown down beyond the hill.

This is a real test of understanding. For four marks, you need these points:

- It is high up
- ... so there is no easy way to see it from above.
- The trees hide the airfield.
- Because you cannot see the runway, a landing plane will seem to be flying down, somewhere behind the hill.

You are free to use quotes if you wish, but (whether or not you do) it is essential that you show understanding and do not just repeat phrases from the passage.

6.   **Why does Hannay 'pray for the coming of darkness' (line 41)?**   **(2)**

> If the plane came back in daylight, the flyers would see him on the dovecot roof and he would be caught.

You need to <u>connect the aeroplane with him being spotted</u>. That is likely to be enough. The example makes certain by explaining that this would lead to him being caught.

You are free to use quotes in answering a question like this, but make sure that your answer includes <u>enough of your own words to show that you understand what is going on</u>. *Don't just copy out a chunk of the passage!*

7.   **The author uses the same technique when describing the sun in line 1 and the 'twilight haze' in line 42.**

(a) What is the name of this technique?   **(2)**

> Personification

Or 'anthropomorphism'!

The sun is 'glaring' in line 1, and the twilight haze 'creeps' in line 42: these things are described <u>as though they are alive</u>.

'Metaphor' would get one mark: the two marks indicate that the examiner is looking for something more specific.

(b) Explain why the example in line 42 is effective.   **(3)**

> 'Crept' suggests the slowness of the sunset and Hannay's frustration with it, as he 'prays' for darkness. On the other hand, the personification of the 'twilight haze' makes it seem threatening, like a huge creature 'creeping' towards him: who knows what dangers the night will bring?

Any two points, with a bit of development, should be fine here.

Notice how the example takes two different approaches to each image:

- What does the personification suggest about the thing ('the twilight haze') itself?
- What does it suggest about the character's (Hannay's) thoughts and feelings?

Here is the example above, with each *main point in italics* and each <u>developed idea underlined</u>:

> *'Crept' suggests the slowness of the sunset* and <u>Hannay's frustration with it, as he 'prays' for darkness</u>. On the other hand, *the personification of the 'twilight haze' makes it seem threatening*, <u>like a huge creature 'creeping'</u> towards him: <u>who knows what dangers the night will bring?</u>

As you can see, this answer is very safe, because there are potentially five things for a marker to tick.

8.   **What are your impressions of Richard Hannay's character (personality)? Give evidence to support your points.**   **(6)**

> Hannay is determined, because although 'thirst' is a 'torment', he stays 'all afternoon' on the roof. He has a strong sense of humour, because even in his desperate state he ironically wishes his pursuers 'joy on their quest'. He loves his country (he is patriotic), because he is made 'furious' by the thought of foreign spies in Scotland.

Based on the six marks available, you should be able to work out that you need three points ('impressions') and a piece of evidence to 'support' each one.

Approach a character question of this sort in the following way:

- Underline several things which the character does, thinks or says. If you need three in the end, aim to find four or five at this point.
- In the margin alongside each one, write a brief note, saying what personality trait it shows ('patient', 'humour', 'determined', 'systematic', 'patriotic', and so on).
- Choose the clearest and most different three (in this case).

You should do all this before writing your answer. People who start writing before they plan often end up with two very similar points, and so lose marks.

Here is the example again, with main points underlined and *supporting evidence in italics*:

> Hannay is determined, because *although 'thirst' is a 'torment', he stays 'all afternoon' on the roof.* He has a strong sense of humour, because *even in his desperate state he ironically wishes his pursuers 'joy on their quest'.* He loves his country (he is patriotic), because *he is made 'furious' by the thought of foreign spies in Scotland.*

Notice how the evidence is usually more than just a quote: there is some explanation of how the evidence supports the point.

9.   **How are the last three sentences made particularly effective?**   **(6)**

> The sentences get shorter and shorter, emphasising how the light grows dimmer and the world quieter. The sound of the aeroplane is made very sinister: its wings 'beat', like a giant bat's or a bird's, helping us to imagine Hannay's fear. The 'twinkling' lights, on the other hand, seem strangely cheerful, which contrasts with Hannay's miserable situation.

Two very well explained points could be enough here, but three are safer. Notice the way that <u>very short quotes</u> are worked into the example.

The three ideas in the example show a range of approaches:

- The first point is based on the *structure* of the writing (how the words are set out on the page, rather than what they mean). However, <u>it connects structure</u> (short sentences) <u>to meaning</u> ('dimmer and … quieter').
- The second point focuses on the way *sounds* are described.
- The third point concentrates on what Hannay can *see*.

Any sensible, supported points should be acceptable.

The Enchanted Castle (paper 4 – type B)

Kathleen, Jimmy and Gerald are on holiday in the West Country. One day they head out to explore a new part of the local area.

'If you call names,' said Jimmy, 'you can go on by yourself.' He added, 'So there!'

'It's part of the game, silly,' explained Gerald kindly. 'You can be Captain tomorrow, so you'd better hold your jaw now, and begin to think about what names you'll call us when it's your turn.'

5   Very slowly and carefully they went down the steps. A vaulted stone arched over their heads. Gerald struck a match when the last step was found to have no edge, and to be, in fact, the beginning of a passage, turning to the left.

'This,' said Jimmy, 'will take us back into the road.'

'Or under it,' said Gerald. 'We've come down eleven steps.'

10   They went on, following their leader, who went very slowly for fear, as he explained, of steps. The passage was very dark.

'I don't half like it!' whispered Jimmy.

Then came a glimmer of daylight that grew and grew, and presently ended in another arch that looked out over a scene so like a picture out of a book about Italy that everyone's breath
15   was taken away, and they simply walked forward silent and staring. A short avenue of cypresses led, widening as it went, to a marble terrace that lay broad and white in the sunlight. The children, blinking, leaned their arms on the broad, flat balustrade and gazed. Immediately below them was a lake just like a lake in *The Beauties of Italy*, a lake with swans and an island and weeping willows; beyond it were green slopes dotted with groves of
20   trees, and amid the trees gleamed the white limbs of statues. Against a little hill to the left was a round white building with pillars, and to the right a waterfall came tumbling down among mossy stones to splash into the lake. Steps fed from the terrace to the water, and other steps to the green lawns beside it. Away across the grassy slopes deer were feeding, and in the distance, where the groves of trees thickened into what looked almost a forest, were
25   enormous shapes of grey stone, like nothing that the children had ever seen before.

'It *is* an enchanted castle,' said Kathleen.

'I don't see any castle,' said Jimmy.

'What do you call that, then?' Gerald pointed to where, beyond a belt of lime-trees, white towers and turrets broke the blue of the sky.

30   'There doesn't seem to be anyone about,' said Kathleen, 'and yet it's all so tidy. I believe it *is* magic!'

'Magic mowing machines,' Jimmy suggested.

'If we were in a book it would be an enchanted castle – certain to be,' said Kathleen.

'It is an enchanted castle,' said Gerald in hollow tones.

35   'But there aren't any.' Jimmy was quite positive.

'How do you know? Do you think there's nothing in the world but what you've seen?' His scorn was crushing.

'I think magic went out when people began to have steam-engines,' Jimmy insisted, 'and newspapers, and telephones and wireless telegraphing.'

40   'Wireless is rather like magic when you come to think of it,' said Gerald.

'Oh, that sort!' Jimmy's contempt was deep.

'Perhaps there's given up being magic because people didn't believe in it any more,' said Kathleen.

'Well, don't let's spoil the show with any silly old not believing,' said Gerald with decision.
45   'I'm going to believe in magic as hard as I can. This is an enchanted garden, and that's an enchanted castle, and I'm jolly well going to explore.'

The dauntless knight then led the way, leaving his ignorant squires to follow or not, just as they jolly well chose. He rolled off the balustrade and strode firmly down towards the lawn, his boots making, as they went, a clatter full of determination. The others followed. There
50   never was such a garden out of a picture or a fairy-tale. They passed quite close by the deer, who only raised their pretty heads to look, and did not seem startled at all. And after a long stretch of turf they passed under the heaped-up heavy masses of lime-trees and came into a rose-garden, bordered with thick, close-cut yew hedges, and lying red and pink and green and white in the sun, like a giant's many-coloured, highly-scented pocket-handkerchief.

55   'I know we shall meet a gardener in a minute, and he'll ask what we're doing here. And then what will you say?' Kathleen asked with her nose in a rose.

'I shall say we have lost our way, and it will be quite true,' said Gerald.

But they did not meet a gardener or anybody else, and the feeling of magic got thicker and thicker, till they were almost afraid of the sound of their feet in the great silent place.

Adapted from *The Enchanted Castle* by E. Nesbit

1.   Why does Kathleen think that the castle is 'enchanted' (line 26)?   (3)

2.   Give a reason why Jimmy might feel that 'magic went out' with the arrival of modern technology (lines 38-39).   (2)

3.   Explain the reference to the 'dauntless knight' and his 'ignorant squires' in line 47.   (3)

4.   Using your own words, describe Gerald's way of walking in lines 48-49.   (2)

5.   (a) Write down the simile which is between lines 44 and 56. (You should not write down the whole sentence.)   (1)

      (b) What do we learn from the comparison in this simile?   (3)

6.   Explain why the children become 'almost afraid of the sound of their own feet' (line 59). Use your own words as far as possible.   (3)

7.   Giving evidence, explain what we learn about the characters of each of the children:

      (a) Jimmy
      (b) Kathleen
      (c) Gerald   (12)

8.   Imagine that you are the owner of the house, watching the children as they approach through the garden. Describe what you see and think. Be as creative as you can.   (8)

[TOTAL 37]

The Enchanted Castle – solutions

1. **Why does Kathleen think that the castle is 'enchanted' (line 26)?**   (3)

> She thinks this because the 'enormous shapes' of the building are 'like nothing' that she has 'ever seen'. 'Shapes' is a vague word, and therefore mysterious. Also, the garden is full of wonderful things such as 'deer' and 'white … statues'.

Focus on the 'why': you need to do *more than simply list things in the garden*. The example mentions the 'statues', for instance, but also explains that they are 'wonderful'. It makes clear why 'enormous shapes' sounds magical.

A single point is unlikely to win three marks by itself. The example makes a couple of comments about the building, but adds the point about the statues and deer for safety's sake.

2. **Give a reason why Jimmy might feel that 'magic went out' with the arrival of modern technology (lines 38-39).**   (2)

> Many things which would once have seemed magical are now done every day, such as talking with a distant person by telephone. Therefore they appear ordinary, not mysterious.

Or

> Because science can do so many things, people assume that there must be a scientific explanation for anything they do not understand, so they do not need magic to explain things.

Or

> Jimmy might think that in modern societies, where technology allows so many things to be made, people are focused on making money and buying objects: they think less about religion, magic, and things of that sort.

Notice the wording of the question: 'why Jimmy might feel' this. In other words, this is asking you to go beyond the information in the passage and suggest your own reason for Jimmy's statement. An important skill in comprehension tests is to recognise when a question *is not asking for an evidence-based answer*; this is quite unusual, but you need to be ready when it happens.

Any sensible answer should be fine.

- One mark for an unsupported statement.
- Two marks for a clear explanation or a point with additional detail.

3.   **Explain the reference to the 'dauntless knight' and his 'ignorant squires' in line 47.**   **(3)**

> Gerald sees himself as a sort of medieval hero, approaching a dangerous castle. He sees the other children as his followers, 'ignorant' because they don't believe in magic.

You need <u>some comment about the words 'knight' and 'squire'</u>. It is helpful if you can draw a connection between Gerald being a 'knight' and the house a 'castle', but some other explanation for the word 'knight' (for example that Gerald is on a quest, or is very brave) is likely to be acceptable.

Even though you may not be familiar with the word 'squire', it should be clear that it describes some sort of follower or assistant. Questions at 11+ frequently test your ability to deal with difficult words, but often <u>you are not expected to know them already: you should use the context to help you.</u>

4.   **Using your own words, describe Gerald's way of walking in lines 48-49.**   **(2)**

> He walks with long, strong, confident steps, which make a loud noise.

You need to explain the words

- 'strode';
- 'firmly';
- 'clatter';

and possibly

- 'determination' (although this might be implied by the rest of your answer).

You are likely to <u>lose half a mark for each missing element</u>. As with any 'own words' question, <u>you will lose marks if your wording is too close to that used in the passage.</u>

5.   **(a) Write down the simile which is between lines 44 and 56. (You should not write down the whole sentence.)**   **(1)**

> like a giant's many-coloured, highly-scented pocket-handkerchief

(b) What do we learn from the comparison in this simile?   **(3)**

> The flowers are arranged like the pattern on a colourful handkerchief. They smell like perfume. The rose garden may well be in the shape of a square or rectangle.

The simplest way to get three marks here is to make <u>three different points</u>, although <u>two points, with some supporting detail for one</u>, might also be adequate.

A reasonable guess about the rose garden should be acceptable here (for example, 'the flowers rustle in the wind like a sheet of cloth').

If you give a different answer to 5(a) you will not get the mark for this part of the question; however, <u>you might still get the marks for (b) if you discuss another comparison effectively</u>.

6.   **Explain why the children become 'almost afraid of the sound of their own feet' (line 59). Use your own words as far as possible.**   **(3)**

> They do not encounter anyone, which is mysterious. The further they go on like this, the more magical the garden seems. They are scared because anything could happen, so they become jumpy, alarmed even by the noises they make themselves.

You could explain one point thoroughly, but <u>two points</u> are a more reliable route to three marks, so long as they have some explanation.

The example makes two points, each with explanation, so it does slightly more than is necessary: it is a safe answer.

7.   **Giving evidence, explain what we learn about the characters of each of the children:**

   (a) Jimmy
   (b) Kathleen
   (c) Gerald   **(12)**

> **(a)** Jimmy is easily annoyed: he says that anybody who calls him names 'can go on' alone. He is sensible: Kathleen thinks the place has been tidied by 'magic', but he suggests 'mowing machines' instead.
>
> **(b)** Kathleen is imaginative: because the place is tidy and they can't see gardeners, she puts it down to 'magic'. She loves nature, putting 'her nose in a rose' to smell it.
>
> **(c)** Gerald is kind, because he says that Jimmy 'can be Captain tomorrow'. He is adventurous, because he is 'jolly well going to explore' and isn't worried about being caught by a gardener.

As you will know by now, you need <u>two points, with evidence for each</u>, for every four marks.

As a reminder, bear these things in mind when writing about character:

- <u>Don't make two similar points about the same character</u> (e.g. 'she is courageous' and 'she is not easily scared').
- <u>Don't</u> just write about <u>the way a character behaves at a particular moment</u>: make a general point about the sort of person they are:
    - o   Don't write 'She likes smelling the rose.'
    - o   Do write 'She likes smelling roses.'
    - o   Even better, write 'She likes flowers.'
    - o   Best of all, write 'She likes nature.'

It isn't necessarily wrong to make similar points about the children. However, their personalities are very different, and answers which do not recognise this are likely to lose marks.

8. **Imagine that you are the owner of the house, watching the children as they approach through the garden. Describe what you see and think. Be as creative as you can.**   **(8)**

> The morning sunlight slips through the window slit, stamping a bright rectangle on the tabletop. I nudge another butterfly into the light and position a new pin above its abdomen. I am about to push down when something distant, above the treetops, catches my eye; my finger is leaking blood as I rush to the window, but I hardly care. I am quivering with excitement.
>
> From the tower I can see them, far away. They tumble from the balustrade beyond the lake, striding towards me, bickering as they come.
>
> Children!
>
> Obnoxious children, dirtying my perfect lawns! I spin away in disgust, but really I am glad. Now at last my plan is working.
>
> The girl – by now I can see that it is a girl – I see her, all of them in fact, between the trees now – she is holding a flower. A flower. My flower!
>
> A servant is shuffling up the staircase. 'Catch them!' I call. I am screaming, I realise. 'Put them to work!'

Your story doesn't need to be as sinister as this one!

You do need to include some details about the children's journey towards the house, and imagine the sort of person who might live there. Do as much as you can to bring them to life.

Here, the owner is pinning butterflies in his high tower, like a Disney villain. The rectangle of light tells you something about the darkness of the tower room, and the word 'stamping' gives a sense of violence.

Notice:

- The use of short and long sentences.
- Various kinds of paragraph.
- The plot: very little happens. The focus is on creating a character.
- Interesting verbs, such as 'stamping', 'tumble', 'bickering', 'spin', 'quivering' and 'shuffling'.

As for any creative writing question, you are likely to lose marks if you make many English mistakes.

Treasure Island (paper 5 – type C)

Jim Hawkins is the cabin boy on a sailing ship, the Hispaniola. It has arrived at an island on which there is said to be treasure. The ship's crew includes the mysterious Long John Silver.

The appearance of the island when I came on deck next morning was altogether changed. Although the breeze had now utterly ceased, we had made a great deal of way during the night and were now lying becalmed about half a mile to the south-east of the low eastern coast. Grey-coloured woods covered a large part of the surface. This even tint was indeed
5   broken up by streaks of yellow sand-break in the lower lands, and by many tall trees of the pine family, out-topping the others – some singly, some in clumps; but the general colouring was uniform and sad. The hills ran up clear above the vegetation in spires of naked rock. All were strangely shaped, and the Spy-glass, which was by three or four hundred feet the tallest on the island, was likewise the strangest in configuration, running up sheer from almost every
10 side and then suddenly cut off at the top like a pedestal to put a statue on.

The Hispaniola was rolling scuppers under* in the ocean swell. The booms were tearing at the blocks, the rudder was banging to and fro, and the whole ship creaking, groaning, and jumping like a manufactory. I had to cling tight to the backstay, and the world turned giddily before my eyes, for though I was a good enough sailor when there was way on, this standing
15 still and being rolled about like a bottle was a thing I never learned to stand without a qualm or so, above all in the morning, on an empty stomach.

Perhaps it was this – perhaps it was the look of the island, with its grey, melancholy woods, and wild stone spires, and the surf that we could both see and hear foaming and thundering on the steep beach – at least, although the sun shone bright and hot, and the shore birds were
20 fishing and crying all around us, and you would have thought anyone would have been glad to get to land after being so long at sea, my heart sank, as the saying is, into my boots; and from the first look onward, I hated the very thought of Treasure Island.

We had a dreary morning's work before us, for there was no sign of any wind, and the boats had to be got out and manned, and the ship warped three or four miles round the corner of the
25 island and up the narrow passage to the haven behind Skeleton Island. I volunteered for one of the boats, where I had, of course, no business. The heat was sweltering, and the men grumbled fiercely over their work. Anderson was in command of my boat, and instead of keeping the crew in order, he grumbled as loud as the worst.

'Well,' he said with an oath, 'it's not forever.'

30 I thought this was a very bad sign, for up to that day the men had gone briskly and willingly about their business; but the very sight of the island had relaxed the cords of discipline.

All the way in, Long John stood by the steersman and conned the ship. He knew the passage like the palm of his hand, and though the man in the chains* got everywhere more water than was down in the chart, John never hesitated once.

35 'There's a strong scour with the ebb,' he said, 'and this here passage has been dug out, in a manner of speaking, with a spade.'

We brought up just where the anchor was in the chart, about a third of a mile from each shore, the mainland on one side and Skeleton Island on the other. The bottom was clean sand. The plunge of our anchor sent up clouds of birds wheeling and crying over the woods, but in
40   less than a minute they were down again and all was once more silent.

The place was entirely land-locked, buried in woods, the trees coming right down to high-water mark, the shores mostly flat, and the hilltops standing round at a distance in a sort of amphitheatre, one here, one there. Two little rivers, or rather two swamps, emptied out into this pond, as you might call it; and the foliage round that part of the shore had a kind of
45   poisonous brightness. From the ship we could see nothing of the house or stockade, for they were quite buried among trees; and if it had not been for the chart on the companion, we might have been the first that had ever anchored there since the island arose out of the seas.

There was not a breath of air moving, nor a sound but that of the surf booming half a mile away along the beaches and against the rocks outside. A peculiar stagnant smell hung over
50   the anchorage – a smell of sodden leaves and rotting tree trunks. I observed the doctor sniffing and sniffing, like someone tasting a bad egg.

'I don't know about treasure,' he said, 'but I'll stake my wig there's fever here.'

If the conduct of the men had been alarming in the boat, it became truly threatening when they had come aboard. They lay about the deck growling together in talk. The slightest order
55   was received with a black look and grudgingly and carelessly obeyed. Even the honest hands must have caught the infection, for there was not one man aboard to mend another. Mutiny, it was plain, hung over us like a thunder-cloud.

From *Treasure Island* by Robert Louis Stevenson

scuppers under: tilted so far that the deck-level drains are underwater on one side
man in the chains: the sailor responsible for testing the water's depth with a weighted line

1.   **What is 'the Spy-glass' (line 8)?**   **(2)**

....

2.   **What does the word 'spires' (line 18) suggest about the island's hilly landscape? Explain your reasoning.**   **(2)**

....

....

3.   'From the first look onward, I hated the very thought of Treasure Island' (line 22).

         Why does Jim 'hate' the island? Why does he find his own feeling surprising? (6)

....

....

....

....

....

....

4.   'The very sight of the island had relaxed the cords of discipline' (line 31).

         Explain what Jim Hawkins means.   (3)

....

....

....

....

....

5.   Discuss the writer's use of alliteration in line 39.   (3)

....

....

....

....

6.   **Explain what the following similes suggest.**

(a) 'like someone tasting a bad egg' (line 51)   (2)

....

....

....

(b) 'like a thundercloud' (line 57)   (2)

....

....

....

7.   **How does the author use descriptions of sounds to make this passage effective?**
                                                                  (6)

....

....

....

....

....

....

....

8.   **Explain what the doctor means in line 52. Use your own words as far as possible.**
                                                                  (3)

....

....

....

9. **Suggest some things which might happen later in the story. Support your ideas carefully, using evidence from the passage.** (9)

....

....

....

....

....

....

....

....

....

....

....

10. **Rewrite the following passage, correcting all the errors in spelling and grammar. Be careful not to add new mistakes of your own.** (12)

We all entered the cave. It was a large, airy plaice, with a little spring and a pool of clear, water, overhung with ferns. The floor was sand. Before a big fire lies Captain Smollett; and in a far corner, only duskily flikered over by the blaze I beheld great heaps of coin and quadrilaterals bilt of bars of gold. That was Flints tresure that we had come so far to seek and that had cost allready the lives of seventeen men from the hispaniola?

....

....

....

....

....

....

....

....

[TOTAL 50]

Treasure Island – solutions

1.   **What is 'the Spy-glass' (line 8)?**   **(2)**

> It is the tallest hill on the island.

- One mark for saying that it is a hill.
- Two marks for saying that it is the tallest hill.

The two marks are an important clue: you cannot just say that it is a hill.

2.   **What does the word 'spires' (line 18) suggest about the island's hilly landscape? Explain your reasoning.**   **(2)**

> Like church spires, the hills are tall and steep-sided.

'Explain' means that you need to recognise <u>what a spire is</u>: the pointed tower on a church. You also need to state <u>what this suggests about the hills</u>.

3.   **'From the first look onward, I hated the very thought of Treasure Island' (line 22).**

      Why does Jim 'hate' the island? Why does he find his own feeling surprising? (6)

> He hates its appearance, with 'grey' woodland and jagged hills, and dislikes the violent sound of the 'surf', which is loud and 'foaming'. He finds this feeling strange because the weather is warm, the birds are lively, and because it should be a relief to reach land after a long journey.

You should aim to give <u>a three mark answer to each half of the question</u>: this approach is safe.

However, a clear answer which <u>addresses both parts</u> of the question (but does not quite include six points) might also be adequate.

- Likewise, an answer which deals with one half of the question more fully than the other might be acceptable, as long as both parts are answered to some extent.

4.   **'The very sight of the island had relaxed the cords of discipline' (line 31).**

     Explain what Jim Hawkins means.   **(3)**

> Discipline is something which holds people together safely, like rope. The thought of arriving at the end of their journey is making the sailors behave less well, as though the rope has been partly untied.

Your answer needs to explain the following:

- What is meant by 'the cords of discipline'.
- What it might mean to 'relax' these cords.
- How 'the sight of the island' has brought about this change.

5.   **Discuss the writer's use of alliteration in line 39.**   **(3)**

You could deal with the two alliterative pairs <u>separately</u>:

> The repeated 'c' sounds ('cords … crying') are like the chattering of the birds. The 'w' sounds ('wheeling … woods') are more like a seagull's longer call.

If you take this approach, you should explain <u>what each sound suggests</u> about the <u>noise</u> or <u>activity</u> of the seagulls, or <u>their effect on the watching sailors</u>.

You might choose to discuss the two 'c' and 'w' sounds <u>together</u>:

> The repeated 'c' sounds ('cords … crying') and 'w' sounds ('wheeling … woods') create a sense of mingled, chaotic noises. This shows the birds' excitement as the anchor hits the water.

<u>If you only discuss the 'c' or the 'w' sounds (not both), you will receive a maximum of two marks</u>.

However you approach this question, the vital thing is that that you talk about <u>the effect of the alliteration *itself*</u> – the repeated consonant sounds – and *don't just talk about the birds and what they do*.

The following answer would probably only receive one mark:

> *The line alliterates with 'c' and 'w' sounds. The birds are scared by the anchor falling and fly about wildly for 'less than a minute'.*

This answer notices the alliteration and discusses the behaviour of the birds, but it <u>doesn't connect these things together</u> in any way.

6.   Explain what the following similes suggest.

(a) 'like someone tasting a bad egg' (line 51)   (2)

> The doctor is sniffing carefully, with a look of disgust – both curious and revolted.

Focus on what the comparison tells you <u>about the doctor</u>, rather than what it might say about a person who sniffs an egg.

Try to make <u>more than one point</u>. The example makes two main points ('carefully … disgust'), and adds some development ('both curious and revolted').

(b) 'like a thundercloud' (line 57)   (2)

> The rebellion will break out suddenly and unexpectedly, with great violence, like a thunderstorm.

You might also say that the prospect of a mutiny is gloomy and terrifying, like the shadow of a thundercloud.

As for part (a), <u>try to make more than one point</u>.

7.   How does the author use descriptions of sounds to make this passage effective?

(6)

> The ship is 'groaning' as it rolls on the waves, as though it is in pain, which mirrors Jim's own discomfort: he feels sick. 'Foaming and thundering' suggests that the island is under attack from the angry ocean. The sailors are described as 'growling': they are a pack, like dogs, who might turn on their leaders.

Notice how the example makes points about <u>three different things</u>:

- the ship
- the sea
- the sailors

You could refer to more than one noise made, for example, by the sea, but it would be difficult to make your points sufficiently different.

If you refer to a noise mentioned in a previous answer (the sea from Q3 or the birds from Q5), <u>make sure to say something new</u>.

When you discuss how a noise is 'effective', be careful to <u>explain what it suggests</u> – what it *adds* to the meaning. Don't just describe what is happening ('the waves are hitting the beach').

8.   **Explain what the doctor means in line 52. Use your own words as far as possible.**

                                                                        (3)

> He can't tell whether there is treasure on the island, but he is very sure (from the smell) that there is lots of disease around.

You should <u>focus on his meaning, rather than on how he expresses it</u>.

You *could* explain that 'I'll stake my wig' means 'I would bet my wig', but you still need to make clear <u>what he really means</u>: he is confident that there is disease around.

- You don't need to put the words 'treasure', 'wig' or 'island' into your own words.
- However, <u>you do need to show that you understand the word 'fever'</u>.

9.   **Suggest some things which might happen later in the story. Support your ideas carefully, using evidence from the passage.**   **(9)**

> The boat struggles to cope with the 'thundering' sea, which makes it 'creak' and 'jump'. Therefore it might break up and sink, leaving the crew stranded on the island. Jim fears 'mutiny' and Anderson thinks that the current situation is 'not forever': the sailors are likely to rebel, killing or imprisoning their leaders. The doctor is certain of 'fever' on the island. If many people become ill, this might calm the sailors and force the officers and crew to work together to survive and escape.

It is very important to realise that questions of this sort <u>are not testing your knowledge of the book</u>. Whether or not you have read *Treasure Island*, you need to make reasonable points, <u>based on the evidence in the passage</u>.

<u>Three points are enough, if each of them has evidence and some extra explanation and/or suggestions</u>.

Markers are likely to be flexible: if one point is brilliantly explained and another is slightly weaker, they should balance each other out.

If you have a fourth point, it will give your answer some security.

Your points might build on each other, forming a plot outline, or they might be separate. They might fit together, or they might present different, even contradictory options.

10. **Rewrite the following passage, correcting all the errors in spelling and grammar. Be careful not to add new mistakes of your own.** **(12)**

We all enterred the cave. It was a large, airy plaice, with a little spring and a pool of clear, water, overhung with ferns. The floor was sand. Before a big fire lies Captain Smollett; and in a far corner, only duskily flikered over by the blaze I beheld great heaps of coin and quadrilaterals bilt of bars of gold. That was Flints tresure that we had come so far to seek and that had cost allready the lives of seventeen men from the hispaniola?

> We all entered the cave. It was a large, airy place, with a little spring and a pool of clear water, overhung with ferns. The floor was sand. Before a big fire lay Captain Smollett; and in a far corner, only duskily flickered over by the blaze, I beheld great heaps of coin and quadrilaterals built of bars of gold. That was Flint's treasure that we had come so far to seek and that had cost already the lives of seventeen men from the Hispaniola.

You need to make the following twelve corrections:

• enterred	entered
• plaice	place
• clear, water	clear water
• lies	lay
• flikered	flickered
• the blaze I beheld	the blaze, I beheld
• bilt	built
• Flints	Flint's
• tresure	treasure
• allready	already
• hispaniola	Hispaniola
• ?	. (Or change 'That was' to 'Was that' and keep the question mark.)

This question should be marked as follows:

- One mark for each corrected mistake.
- Half a mark for each mistake identified but wrongly corrected.
- Minus one mark for each new mistake added.

Minor changes which make the text neither better nor worse (for example, changing 'coin' to 'coins' or 'cost already' to 'already cost') should not gain or lose marks.

Dracula (paper 6 – type C)

Jonathan Harker, an English lawyer, is visiting a new client. This mysterious nobleman lives in a castle in Transylvania, which nowadays is part of Romania.

Jonathan Harker's Journal, 5 May

I must have been asleep, for certainly if I had been fully awake I must have noticed the approach of such a remarkable place. In the gloom the courtyard looked of considerable size, and as several dark ways led from it under great round arches, it perhaps seemed bigger than
5   it really is. I have not yet been able to see it by daylight.

I stood close to a great door, old and studded with large iron nails, and set in a projecting doorway of massive stone. I could see even in the dim light that the stone was massively carved, but that the carving had been much worn by time and weather. As I stood, the driver jumped again into his seat and shook the reins; the horses started forward, and trap and all
10   disappeared down one of the dark openings.

I stood in silence where I was, for I did not know what to do. Of bell or knocker there was no sign; through these frowning walls and dark window openings it was not likely that my voice could penetrate. The time I waited seemed endless, and I felt doubts and fears crowding upon me. What sort of place had I come to, and among what kind of people? What sort of grim
15   adventure was it on which I had embarked? I began to rub my eyes and pinch myself to see if I were awake. It all seemed like a horrible nightmare to me, and I expected that I should suddenly awake, and find myself at home, with the dawn struggling in through the windows, as I had now and again felt in the morning after a day of overwork. But my flesh answered the pinching test, and my eyes were not to be deceived. I was indeed awake and among the
20   Carpathian mountains. All I could do now was to be patient, and to wait the coming of the morning.

Just as I had come to this conclusion I heard a heavy step approaching behind the great door, and saw through the chinks the gleam of a coming light. Then there was the sound of rattling chains and the clanking of massive bolts drawn back. A key was turned with the loud grating
25   noise of long disuse, and the great door swung back.

Within, stood a tall old man, clean shaven save for a long white moustache, and clad in black from head to foot, without a single speck of colour about him anywhere. He held in his hand an antique silver lamp, in which the flame burned without chimney or globe of any kind, throwing long quivering shadows as it flickered in the draught of the open door. The old man
30   motioned me in with his right hand with a courtly gesture, saying in excellent English, but with a strange intonation:

'Welcome to my house! Enter freely and of your own will!' He made no motion of stepping to meet me, but stood like a statue, as though his gesture of welcome had fixed him into stone.

35   'Count Dracula?' He bowed in a courtly way as he replied:

'I am Dracula; and I bid you welcome, Mr. Harker, to my house. Come in; the night air is chill, and you must need to eat and rest.'

***

40   By this time I had finished my supper, and by my host's desire had drawn up a chair by the fire and begun to smoke a cigar which he offered me, at the same time excusing himself that he did not smoke.

His face was very strong, with thin nose and peculiarly arched nostrils; with lofty domed forehead, and hair growing scantily round the temples but profusely elsewhere. His eyebrows were very massive, almost meeting over the nose, and with bushy hair that seemed to curl.
45   The mouth, so far as I could see it under the heavy moustache, was fixed and rather cruel-looking, with peculiarly sharp white teeth; these protruded over the lips. For the rest, his ears were pale, and at the tops extremely pointed; the chin was broad and strong, and the cheeks firm though thin. The general effect was one of extraordinary paleness.

As the Count leaned over me and his hands touched me, I could not repress a shudder. It may
50   have been that his breath was rank, but a horrible feeling came over me, which, do what I would, I could not conceal. The Count, evidently noticing it, drew back; and with a grim sort of smile, which showed more than he had yet done his protuberant teeth, sat himself down again on his own side of the fireplace. We were both silent for a while; and as I looked towards the window I saw the first dim streak of the coming dawn. There seemed a strange
55   stillness over everything; but as I listened I heard as if from down below in the valley the howling of many wolves. The Count's eyes gleamed, and he said:

'Listen to them – the children of the night. What music they make!' Seeing, I suppose, some expression in my face strange to him, he added:

'Ah, sir, you dwellers in the city cannot enter into the feelings of the hunter.'

Adapted from *Dracula* by Bram Stoker

1.   **Why does the narrator say that he 'must have been asleep' (line 2)?**   (2)

2.   **Explain why the experience feels 'like a horrible nightmare' to the narrator (line 16).**   (4)

3.   **Give the meanings of the following words:**

   (a) courtly (lines 30 & 35)   (1)
   (b) protuberant (line 52)   (1)

4.   **How much can we trust the narrator's description of the castle in lines 2-10? Give evidence to support your ideas.**   (5)

5.   (a) Write down a simile from lines 22-59.   (1)
     (b) In what ways is this simile effective?   (3)

6.   How does the fact that this passage is set at night make it effective?   (4)

7.   How does the author use a range of senses to bring this passage to life? Refer to at least three different senses in your answer. (These are usually listed as sight, hearing, smell, taste and touch.) Do not repeat ideas from your previous answers.   (8)

8.   What do lines 49-59 suggest to you about Count Dracula's personality? Explain your points in detail, giving evidence from the text. Do not repeat ideas from your previous answers.   (9)

9.   The following passage has no punctuation. Rewrite it correctly. Do not add or remove any words.   (8)

there he lay but looking as if his youth had been half renewed the mouth was redder than ever for on the lips were gouts of fresh blood they trickled from the corners of the mouth and ran over the chin and neck

10.   Rewrite the following passage with correct punctuation.   (4)

'See he said they come quickly; they are flogging the horses, and galloping as hard as they can.'

[TOTAL 50]

Dracula – solutions

1.   **Why does the narrator say that he 'must have been asleep' (line 2)?**   **(2)**

> If he had not been asleep, he would have seen the castle as he came up to it, because it is so large and 'remarkable'.

Because there are two marks available, you need to do more than explain that he should have seen it while approaching: you must make clear *why* he thinks he should have seen it.

The question does not specify 'own words'. However, it is always important to show that you understand the passage.

- You should not expect to get full marks if you simply copy out large parts of lines 2-3.

2.   **Explain why the experience feels 'like a horrible nightmare' to the narrator (line 16).**   **(4)**

> He cannot see a 'bell or knocker' and thinks that nobody will hear him, so he feels trapped in the courtyard. The wait seems 'endless', like in a dream where time stretches.

Any sensible, evidence-based idea is acceptable here. For example, you might refer to the 'doubts and fears' which 'crowd' Harker.

For four marks, you need to make two points with evidence and perhaps some explanation.

It is *usually* good practice to address *all parts of a quotation* given in a question. In this case, a 'nightmare' is by definition 'horrible', so this principle doesn't really apply.

However, to properly explain the word 'nightmare', you do need to consider:

- why the experience is *unpleasant* (the first sentence of the example);
- why the experience is *dreamlike* (the second sentence of the example).

A pernickety marker would expect to see both of these elements in your answer. Others might be more lenient.

3.   **Give the meanings of the following words:**

     (a) courtly (lines 30 & 35)   **(1)**

> with old-fashioned good manners

As this is only a one mark question, anything to do with good manners (polite, old, aristocratic, etc.) should be enough.

(b) protuberant (line 52)   **(1)**

> sticking out

Not 'funny-looking'!

Line 46 ('protruded over the lips') is a strong clue, if you notice it. (*This is why you need to read the whole text carefully before you start writing answers.*)

4.   **How much can we trust the narrator's description of the castle in lines 2-10? Give evidence to support your ideas.**   **(5)**

> He gives lots of detail, such as 'studded with large iron nails', which suggests that he has remembered everything carefully. On the other hand, he says that perhaps it 'seemed bigger' than it was because of all the dark openings. Overall, I trust him on the details, but think he might be wrong about the size of things.

You need two points with evidence; the fifth mark is for a decent attempt to state 'how much' you trust the narrator.

You might say that you do trust him, or that you don't, or that (as in the example) you partly trust him.

Your two points can both support the same opinion if you like. However, for a debate/opinion question, it is always strongest to consider both points of view. This approach also makes your answer easy to structure (*for – against – decide*, for example).

5.   **(a) Write down a simile from lines 22-59.**   **(1)**

> 'stood like a statue'

(b) In what ways is this simile effective?   **(3)**

> It shows how rigid ('fixed') Dracula is. It also makes him seem unwelcoming to Jonathan Harker, like the silent stone courtyard.

If you give a different answer to 5(a) you will not get the mark for this part of the question; however, you are still able to get the marks for (b) if you answer this second part well.

When discussing how a simile is 'effective' in describing a character, you should ask yourself what it adds to your understanding of them.

As usual for a three mark explanation, you probably need to make two points.

6.   **How does the fact that this passage is set at night make it effective?**   **(4)**

> The darkness creates a sense of mystery. For example, the 'dark ways' could lead anywhere from the courtyard. The sounds of the night add to the sense that Harker is in a kind of waking 'nightmare', for example when the wolves 'howl' in the valley.

Of course, this needs <u>two points with evidence</u>.

Ideally, your points will be slightly more than just a simple statement: <u>they should be explained</u>.

- For example, *how* do the 'dark ways' 'create a sense of mystery'? It is because they 'could lead anywhere'.

Notice how the example finds two different points by talking about what Harker <u>sees</u> and what he <u>hears</u>.

7.   **How does the author use a range of senses to bring this passage to life? Refer to at least three different senses in your answer. (These are usually listed as sight, hearing, smell, taste and touch.) Do not repeat ideas from your previous answers.**
                                                             (8)

> Stoker uses light (sight) to contrast with the darkness. For example, the 'gleam' of light through the door is a sign of hope that Harker will be able to escape the awful courtyard. He uses smell when the count's breath is described as 'rank'. This makes Dracula seem disgusting, but it is also very mysterious: he shows his teeth after Harker smells his breath, suggesting that he has been eating something strange and horrible. Touch is referred to when the narrator 'pinches' himself. This shows us how far Harker does not trust his eyes, but also helps to prove to the reader that these are not in fact dream events.

Bearing in mind that the question asks you to discuss 'at least three different senses', and that there are eight marks available, your options are:

- Discuss <u>three examples very fully</u>.
- Discuss <u>four in slightly less depth</u>.

The example deals with three.

If you are looking to get three marks for a single idea, you must <u>ensure that you make two points when explaining</u>, and that these points are *not simply re-wordings of each other*.

The first idea in the example would probably be worth three marks (definitely two); the others are clearly worth three each.

The passage contains examples of <u>sight</u>, <u>hearing</u>, <u>smell</u> and <u>touch</u>, though not taste.

If you make a fourth point, it may refer (using a new example) to a sense that you have already discussed.

- For this and the next question, bear in mind the instruction <u>not to 'repeat ideas from your previous answers'</u>. Depending on how closely you repeat an earlier idea, you will lose some or all of the marks available for that point.

8. **What do lines 49-59 suggest to you about Count Dracula's personality? Explain your points in detail, giving evidence from the text. Do not repeat ideas from your previous answers.** **(9)**

> Dracula gives a 'grim smile' when Harker has smelled his foul breath. This suggests that he is proud of his ability to provoke a strong reaction in other people: perhaps it gives him a feeling of power. He describes the wolves' howling as 'music', and suggests that he understands 'the feelings of the hunter': he regards killing as noble, even beautiful, and sees himself as being in some ways similar to a wild animal. He sits in silence 'for a while', suggesting that he is patient and thoughtful. He likes to wait and see how other people will act, perhaps because he is interested in learning about their behaviour.

You *could* make five brief points with evidence, but the nine marks are a strong hint that <u>three thoroughly explained ideas</u> are expected.

It is in fact rather difficult to find even three points in this section.

- Bear in mind that what somebody *does not do* can reveal a lot about them (hence the point about Dracula's silence).

It might be possible to find two different points in Dracula's discussion of the wolves.

9. **The following passage has no punctuation. Rewrite it correctly. Do not add or remove any words.** **(8)**

there he lay but looking as if his youth had been half renewed the mouth was redder than ever for on the lips were gouts of fresh blood they trickled from the corners of the mouth and ran over the chin and neck

> There he lay, but looking as if his youth had been half renewed. The mouth was redder than ever, for on the lips were gouts of fresh blood. They trickled from the corners of the mouth and ran over the chin and neck.

This describes Count Dracula asleep in his coffin, after drinking the blood of a victim.

Instead of the two full stops between sentences, you could use semicolons (;) in either place or both. In this case, you would not put a capital letter afterwards.

Any of the full stops could also be replaced by an exclamation mark (!).

- Take away a mark for each missing or incorrect use of punctuation.
- Take away a mark for any extra mistake.

10.   **Rewrite the following passage with correct punctuation.**   **(4)**

'See he said they come quickly; they are flogging the horses, and galloping as hard as they can.'

'See,' he said, 'they come quickly; they are flogging the horses, and galloping as hard as they can.'

Or

'See!' he said. 'They come quickly; they are flogging the horses, and galloping as hard as they can.'

Other changes to the punctuation are likely to be acceptable (for example, changing the semicolon into a full stop), <u>so long as they do not introduce new mistakes</u>. However, it is safer not to make unnecessary changes.

- <u>Minus one mark for each correction missed or for each error</u>.

You shouldn't lose a mark if you swap the comma and the speech mark (*'See', he said* ...), although this is arguably incorrect.

The Lost World (paper 7 – type D)

Edward Malone is describing a journey into the Amazon rainforest with two Professors, Challenger and Summerlee, and Lord John Roxton, an explorer. In this section, they are walking across a high plateau – a raised, flat area – cut off from the outside world by steep cliffs.

We may have travelled two or three miles in all, keeping to the right of the line of the stream, when we came upon a considerable opening in the trees. A belt of brushwood led up to a tangle of rocks – the whole plateau was strewn with boulders. We were walking slowly towards these rocks, among bushes which reached over our waists, when we became aware of

5   a strange low gabbling and whistling sound, which filled the air with a constant clamour and appeared to come from some spot immediately before us. Lord John held up his hand as a signal for us to stop, and he made his way swiftly, stooping and running, to the line of rocks. We saw him peep over them and give a gesture of amazement. Then he stood staring as if forgetting us, so utterly entranced was he by what he saw. Finally he waved us to come on,

10   holding up his hand as a signal for caution. His whole bearing made me feel that something wonderful but dangerous lay before us.

Creeping to his side, we looked over the rocks. The place into which we gazed was a pit, and may, in the early days, have been one of the smaller volcanic blow-holes of the plateau. It was bowl-shaped and at the bottom, some hundreds of yards from where we lay, were pools

15   of green-scummed, stagnant water, fringed with bullrushes. It was a weird place in itself, but its occupants made it seem like a scene from the Seven Circles of Dante. The place was a rookery of pterodactyls. There were hundreds of them congregated within view. All the bottom area round the water-edge was alive with their young ones, and with hideous mothers brooding upon their leathery, yellowish eggs. From this crawling flapping mass of obscene

20   reptilian life came the shocking clamour which filled the air and the horrible, musty odour which turned us sick. But above, perched each upon its own stone, tall, gray, and withered, more like dead and dried specimens than actual living creatures, sat the horrible males, absolutely motionless save for the rolling of their red eyes or an occasional snap of their rat-trap beaks as a dragon-fly went past them. Their huge, membranous wings were closed by

25   folding their fore-arms, so that they sat like gigantic old women, wrapped in hideous web-coloured shawls, and with their ferocious heads protruding above them. Large and small, not less than a thousand of these filthy creatures lay in the hollow before us.

Our professors would gladly have stayed there all day, so entranced were they by this opportunity of studying the life of a prehistoric age. They pointed out the fish and dead birds

30   lying about among the rocks as proving the nature of the food of these creatures, and I heard them congratulating each other on having cleared up the point why the bones of this flying dragon are found in such great numbers in certain well-defined areas, as in the Cambridge Green-sand, since it was now seen that, like penguins, they lived in gregarious* fashion.

Finally, however, Challenger, bent upon proving some point which Summerlee had

35   contested, thrust his head over the rock and nearly brought destruction upon us all. In an instant the nearest male gave a shrill, whistling cry, and flapped its twenty-foot span of leathery wings as it soared up into the air. The females and young ones huddled together beside the water, while the whole circle of sentinels rose one after the other and sailed off into the sky. It was a wonderful sight to see at least a hundred creatures of such enormous

40   size and hideous appearance all swooping like swallows with swift, shearing wing-strokes above us; but soon we realized that it was not one on which we could afford to linger. At first the great brutes flew round in a huge ring, as if to make sure what the exact extent of the danger might be. Then, the flight grew lower and the circle narrower, until they were whizzing round and round us, the dry, rustling flap of their huge slate-coloured wings filling

45   the air with a volume of sound that made me think of Hendon aerodrome upon a race day.

'Make for the wood and keep together,' cried Lord John, clubbing his rifle. 'The brutes mean mischief.'

The moment we attempted to retreat, the circle closed in upon us, until the tips of the wings of those nearest to us nearly touched our faces. We beat at them with the stocks of our guns,

50   but there was nothing solid or vulnerable to strike. Then suddenly out of the whizzing, slate-coloured circle a long neck shot out, and a fierce beak made a thrust at us. Another and another followed. Summerlee gave a cry and put his hand to his face, from which the blood was streaming. I felt a prod at the back of my neck, and turned dizzy with the shock. Challenger fell, and as I stooped to pick him up I was again struck from behind and dropped

55   on the top of him. At the same instant I heard the crash of Lord John's elephant-gun, and, looking up, saw one of the creatures with a broken wing struggling upon the ground, spitting and gurgling at us with a wide-opened beak and blood-shot, goggled eyes, like some devil in a medieval picture. Its comrades had flown higher at the sudden sound, and were circling above our heads.

60   'Now,' cried Lord John, 'now for our lives!'

We staggered through the brushwood, and even as we reached the trees the harpies were on us again. Summerlee was knocked down, but we tore him up and rushed among the trunks. Once there we were safe, for those huge wings had no space for their sweep beneath the branches. As we limped homewards, sadly mauled and discomfited, we saw them for a long

65   time flying at a great height against the deep blue sky above our heads, soaring round and round, no bigger than wood-pigeons, with their eyes no doubt still following our progress. At last, however, as we reached the thicker woods they gave up the chase, and we saw them no more.

'A most interesting and convincing experience,' said Challenger, as we halted beside the

70   brook and he bathed a swollen knee. 'We are exceptionally well informed, Summerlee, as to the habits of the enraged pterodactyl.'

Adapted from *The Lost World* by Sir Arthur Conan Doyle

gregarious: sociable

1.   **Using your own words as far as possible, describe the landscape where the pterodactyls' pit is located. Base your answer on lines 2-4.**   **(2)**

....

....

....

2.   **What do the pterodactyls eat?**   **(2)**

....

3.   **Write down the meanings of the following words, as used in the passage:**

(a) gabbling (line 5)   ....   **(2)**

(b) bearing (line 10)   ....   **(2)**

4.   **How does Conan Doyle make the female and male pterodactyls seem 'hideous' in lines 17-26?**

Females: ....

....

....

....

....   **(4)**

Males: ....

....

....

....

....   **(4)**

5.   *'I heard them congratulating each other on having cleared up the point why the bones of this flying dragon are found in such great numbers in certain well-defined areas, as in the Cambridge Green-sand, since it was now seen that, like penguins, they lived in gregarious [sociable] fashion.'*

Explain, using your own words as far as possible, why the two professors congratulate each other.   **(4)**

....

....

....

....

....

....

6.   **Why can't the travellers drive the pterodactyls away by hitting them with the stocks of their guns?**   **(2)**

....

....

....

7.   **Choose two verbs from lines 48-59 which you find particularly effective. Give your reasons for choosing each one.**

Verb one: ....

....

....

.... **(3)**

Verb two: ....

....

....

.... **(3)**

8.   **Explain in your own words how the explorers know that they are 'safe' (line 63).**   **(2)**

....

....

9.   **Compare the characters of Professor Challenger and Lord John.**   **(6)**

....

....

....

....

....

....

....

....

10.   **In lines 34-59, how are the pterodactyls made to seem**

   (a) familiar to the reader?   **(4)**

....

....

....

....

   (b) unfamiliar to the reader?   **(4)**

....

....

....

....

11.   **How is this passage made exciting? Give evidence to support your points.**   **(6)**

....

....

....

....

....

....

....

....

[TOTAL 50]

The Lost World – solutions

1.   **Using your own words as far as possible, describe the landscape where the pterodactyls' pit is located. Base your answer on lines 2-4.**   **(2)**

> There is a large clearing in the forest, with patches of scrub and a heap of large stones.

You should be <u>as specific as possible</u> about the area where the pit is located, as described in lines 2-4. *Comments about the whole plateau will not get marks.*

Similarly, be careful to talk only <u>about the physical landscape</u> – not about the noises of the pterodactyls, for example.

You will lose marks if you do not include <u>all</u> of the following features:

- the 'opening in the trees'
- the 'brushwood'
- the 'boulders'

As you know by now, 'using your own words' means that you should change the passage's wording <u>enough that you show clear understanding</u>.

2.   **What do the pterodactyls eat?**   **(2)**

> They eat 'fish' and 'birds'.

It is unusual for the second question in a comprehension not to refer to the first few lines, but you need to be ready for unusual challenges like this.

In all other ways, this is a simple question.

3.   **Write down the meanings of the following words, as used in the passage:**

    (a) gabbling (line 5)   **(2)**

> Rapid and confusing

    (b) bearing (line 10)   **(2)**

> The way he holds his body

There are two marks for each of these because they are quite tricky.

<u>A partly correct answer would get one mark</u>.

If you say that 'gabbling' is a noun, or that 'bearing' is a verb (they could be, in a different context), you might lose a mark. For this reason, <u>you must check words 'as used in the passage'</u>, even if you think you know their meanings.

4.   How does Conan Doyle make the female and male pterodactyls seem 'hideous' in lines 17-26?

Females: (4)

> They are a 'crawling flapping mass', like a cluster of maggots in rotten meat: they don't seem to have separate personalities. Conan Doyle helps us to imagine their smell by describing their 'musty' odour: it is strong enough to make the explorers feel 'sick'.

Males: (4)

> The sound of the males' beaks when they 'snap' is vicious. The pterodactyls are described as having 'shawls', which makes them seem almost human. Therefore the fact that they are 'withered' and seem 'dead' is particularly disturbing.

Essentially, each of the examples makes <u>two points, each with evidence</u>.

However, notice how in each case there is an extra effort <u>to link the answer to the word 'hideous'</u> in the question. The final part of each one does this.

Also notice how the examples use <u>a range of senses</u> (sight, smell, hearing). If you treat the senses (sight, hearing, smell, taste, touch) as a checklist, you will find ideas in a text that you might otherwise have missed.

5.   *'I heard them congratulating each other on having cleared up the point why the bones of this flying dragon are found in such great numbers in certain well-defined areas, as in the Cambridge Green-sand, since it was now seen that, like penguins, they lived in gregarious [sociable] fashion.'*

   Explain, using your own words as far as possible, why the two professors congratulate each other.   (4)

> They have solved an old question: why pterodactyl bones are found all together in particular places. They have discovered that the creatures live together in big groups.

You need to explain clearly:

- what the professors' question was;
- how this discovery has resolved it.

You do not need to mention the 'Cambridge Green-sand' or the comparison to penguins.

This is not the sort of question for which you need four different points. <u>The marks are for showing full, clear understanding</u>.

6.   **Why can't the travellers drive the pterodactyls away by hitting them with the stocks of their guns?**   **(2)**

> The only parts of the animals within reach are their leathery wings. There is nothing 'solid' to hit (such as bones) and the leather is strong (not 'vulnerable').

There are several ways in which you could express the main idea here. If you are clear and correct, you will get both marks.

You do not need to quote; if you do (as in the example), make sure that you <u>do not simply copy the relevant section</u>. You must show that you *understand*.

7.   **Choose two verbs from lines 48-59 which you find particularly effective. Give your reasons for choosing each one.**

Verb one: **(3)**

> 'Shot out' is effective because it conveys the speed and violence of the reptiles. The word 'shot' makes their beaks seem dangerous like guns, which contrasts with the uselessness of the travellers' weapons when they try to beat the pterodactyls away with them.

There is <u>one mark for finding a verb</u>. The other <u>two are for your explanation</u>.

A very generous marker might give three marks for the first sentence of the example. However, *only writing that much would be a gamble*. For a three mark question, it is wise to explain more fully.

- 'Shot out' is an example of a **phrasal verb**: a phrase consisting of a verb ('shot') and another element ('out'), which together have a different meaning from the verb by itself.

Verb two: **(3)**

> 'Gurgling' is effective because it creates sympathy for the pterodactyl (it suggests great pain), at the same time as sounding 'hideous', like a 'devil'. As an onomatopoeia, it helps the reader to imagine the animal's sound.

As in the previous example, the first sentence might be enough by itself; the second makes sure.

- **Onomatopoeia**: a word that sounds like the thing it describes.

8.   **Explain in your own words how the explorers know that they are 'safe' (line 63).**
                                                                                      (2)

> The trees are too close together for the pterodactyls, with their huge wings, to fly between them.

You just need to show that you understand the concept. You don't need to write a great deal.

However, it would not be enough just to say that the trees are 'close together': you must explain <u>why this makes the travellers feel 'safe'</u>.

Be careful here, as with any 'own words' question.

9.   Compare the characters of Professor Challenger and Lord John.   **(6)**

> Challenger is calm and understated, for example describing their near-death experience as 'interesting'. On the other hand, Lord John is excitable. At one point he gives a 'gesture of amazement' and later he cries, 'now for our lives!' Lord John is more careful than Challenger, 'peeping' over the rocks. The other man carelessly 'thrusts his head over' the edge, disturbing the pterodactyls.

You need to make <u>two comparisons, with evidence</u>.

A comparison ought to include <u>a point about the character of each man</u>, with <u>evidence on each side</u>. Therefore (if this is done twice), this looks like an eight mark question. This means that you have <u>some margin for error</u>: if a couple of pieces of evidence are missing, for example, you might still be okay.

<u>Be careful not to make your two points too similar.</u>

This question is tricky because the men's personalities are quite complex. For example, Lord John is 'excitable', but he still acts more cautiously than the 'calm and understated' Challenger. This is one reason why Conan Doyle is an excellent writer: even in adventure stories like this, he creates characters with the inconsistencies and subtleties of real people.

10.   In lines 34-59, how are the pterodactyls made to seem:-

(a) familiar to the reader?   **(4)**

> They 'swoop like swallows', implying that, apart from their size, they are like familiar British birds. They sound like an aeroplane 'race day', which makes the noise of their prehistoric wings seem surprisingly similar to a modern invention.

This example takes the easy route, finding those moments when Conan Doyle compares the pterodactyls to familiar present-day (or early twentieth century) sights and sounds.

It makes <u>two points, with evidence for each</u>. Notice that it is careful to explain <u>how</u> each point creates a sense of familiarity.

(b) unfamiliar to the reader?   **(4)**

> The 'dry, rustling flap' of the reptiles' wings is unlike the sound of any familiar large flying creature. The wounded animal is compared to 'some devil': it can't be likened to an earthly being.

This is a little more difficult than part (a). However, if you give two examples and make a good fist of explaining how they create unfamiliarity, you ought to be fine.

11.   How is this passage made exciting? Give evidence to support your points.   (6)

> The author builds the reader's curiosity by delaying important information: the 'bowl-shaped' pit is described in detail before the pterodactyls are mentioned. Dramatic sounds such as the 'shrill, whistling cry' emphasise the anger of the reptiles. Physical feelings ('a prod at … my neck') allow us to imagine how the explorers feel as the creatures try to kill them.

Needless to say, you have to answer as though you find the passage exciting, even if you do not!

The example makes two points about the senses (sound and touch in this case).

It also talks about the passage's structure (how it is put together), when it discusses the way that key information is delayed.

Other structural points might involve:

- the use of long/short sentences
- punctuation

You might also think about:

- formal techniques such as alliteration
- the use of language, such as strong verbs and adjectives

Do not make the mistake of just stating that something is interesting or exciting: you must explain how this is achieved.

Here is an example of a very weak answer to the question, even though it gives plenty of evidence:

> *The author gives lots of information about the 'bowl-shaped' pit and the landscape around it, for example describing the 'boulders'. He makes it exciting by using strong adjectives such as 'shrill'. He describes feelings such as the 'prod' at one person's 'neck', which is also exciting.*

Can you see the problems here?

- The first point has nothing to do with excitement.
- The second point says that the adjectives are exciting, without giving any reason why.
- The final point makes the same mistake again.

This answer would be worth three marks – maybe four, if the sun is shining and the examiner is in a happy mood.

Silas Marner (paper 8 – type D)

Silas Marner is a weaver who lives alone in a tiny house, just outside the village of Raveloe. All his money, which he has been saving for years, was recently stolen from him.

He thought he had been too long standing at the door and looking out. Turning towards the hearth, where the two logs had fallen apart and sent forth only a red uncertain glimmer, he seated himself on his fireside chair, and was stooping to push his logs together, when, to his blurred vision, it seemed as if there were gold on the floor in front of the hearth. Gold! – his

5   own gold – brought back to him as mysteriously as it had been taken away! He felt his heart begin to beat violently, and for a few moments he was unable to stretch out his hand and grasp the restored treasure. The heap of gold seemed to glow and get larger beneath his agitated gaze. He leaned forward at last, and stretched forth his hand; but instead of the hard coin with the familiar resisting outline, his fingers encountered soft warm curls.

10   In utter amazement, Silas fell on his knees and bent his head low to examine the marvel: it was a sleeping child – a round, fair thing, with soft yellow rings all over its head. Could this be his little sister come back to him in a dream – his little sister whom he had carried about in his arms for a year before she died, when he was a small boy without shoes or stockings?

That was the first thought that darted across Silas's blank wonderment. Was it a dream? He

15   rose to his feet again, pushed his logs together, and, throwing on some dried leaves and sticks, raised a flame; but the flame did not disperse the vision – it only lit up more distinctly the little round form of the child, and its shabby clothing. It was very much like his little sister. Silas sank into his chair powerless. How and when had the child come in without his knowledge? He had never been beyond the door.

20   But there was a cry on the hearth: the child had awakened, and Marner stooped to lift it on his knee. It clung round his neck, and burst louder and louder into that mingling of cries with 'Mammy' by which little children express the bewilderment of waking. Silas pressed it to him, and almost unconsciously uttered sounds of hushing tenderness, while he thought that some of his porridge, which had got cool by the dying fire, would do to feed the child with if

25   it were only warmed up a little.

He had plenty to do through the next hour. The porridge, sweetened with some dry brown sugar from an old store, stopped the cries of the little one, and made her lift her blue eyes with a wide quiet gaze at Silas, as he put the spoon into her mouth. Presently she slipped from his knee and began to toddle about, but with a pretty stagger that made Silas jump up and

30   follow her lest she should fall against anything that would hurt her. But she only fell in a sitting posture on the ground, and began to pull at her boots, looking up at him with a crying face as if the boots hurt her. He took her on his knee again, but it was some time before it occurred to Silas's dull mind that the wet boots were the problem, pressing on her warm ankles. He got them off with difficulty, and baby was at once happily occupied with the

35   mystery of her own toes, inviting Silas, with much chuckling, to consider the mystery too.

But the wet boots had at last suggested to Silas that the child had been walking on the snow. He raised the child in his arms, and went to the door. As soon as he had opened it, there was the cry of 'Mammy' again, which Silas had not heard since the child's first hungry waking.

40 Bending forward, he could just discern the marks made by the little feet on the snow, and he followed their track to the furze bushes. 'Mammy!' the little one cried again and again, stretching itself forward so as almost to escape from Silas's arms, before he himself was aware that there was something more than the bush before him – that there was a human body, with the head sunk low in the furze, and half-covered with the shaken snow.

Adapted from *Silas Marner* by George Eliot (pen name of Mary Ann Evans)

1. Why is Silas 'unable to stretch out his hand' (line 6)?   (3)

2. Write down the meanings of the following words and phrases:

    (a) 'blank wonderment' (line 14)   (2)
    (b) 'disperse' (line 16)   (1)
    (c) 'bewilderment' (line 22)   (1)
    (d) 'discern' (line 39)   (1)

3. 'Silas fell on his knees and bent his head low to examine the marvel' (line 10).

    What does this suggest about his thoughts and feelings at this point?   (3)

4. How does Eliot make us feel sympathetic to (care about) the crying child in lines 21-22?   (4)

5. In your opinion, roughly how old is the child? Give evidence to support your points.   (5)

6. Based on the evidence in this passage, do you think Silas cares more about his lost gold or about the child?   (8)

7. What are your impressions of the child's personality? Explain your points carefully, giving evidence from the passage.   (8)

8. How does the author create a sense of confusion and excitement in paragraph 1 (lines 1-9)?   (6)

9.   **Continue the story for around 10-15 lines. Do not introduce any new characters. You will be marked on the quality of your writing and the way in which you develop ideas from the passage.**   **(8)**

[TOTAL 50]

Silas Marner – solutions

This paper is challenging (it is closer to 13+ level than 11+) but has been included here so that even an exceptionally difficult 11+ will not be a shock in the exam hall. If you do poorly in it, don't worry. If you do well, you should be pleased.

1.   Why is Silas 'unable to stretch out his hand' (line 6)?   (3)

> Silas is so excited by the thought that his gold has been 'brought back to him' that he feels overwhelmed ('his heart began to beat violently') and is frozen to the spot.

You need to explain

- how Silas feels;
- why he feels this way;
- why it affects his ability to act.

You may give evidence to support your points, or not, as you choose. However, when in doubt, it is <u>always safest to do so</u> (unless the question asks for your 'own words').

2.   Write down the meanings of the following words and phrases:

(a) 'blank wonderment' (line 14)   (2)

> A lack of thoughts, because he is so amazed.

There are two marks for this because you need to show understanding of 'blank' and 'wonderment'.

(b) 'disperse' (line 16)   (1)

> get rid of

'Write down' means that you do not need to use full sentences.

(c) 'bewilderment' (line 22)   (1)

> confusion

Be careful not to mix up 'wonderment' from (a) (which means 'amazement') with 'bewilderment'.

(d) 'discern' (line 39)   (1)

> see

Or 'recognize', 'notice', 'make out', etc.

3.   'Silas fell on his knees and bent his head low to examine the marvel' (line 10).

       What does this suggest about his thoughts and feelings at this point?   (3)

> Silas is so surprised to find a child in his house that he falls to the floor. He is fascinated by it, so wants to look at it as closely as possible. Perhaps he doesn't quite believe that it is real.

Or

> Silas expects this to be his gold, brought back to him 'mysteriously' – but when he reaches out and finds the head of a child, it seems even more amazing, like a miracle; so he falls to the ground and bows his head before the child as though he is praying to God.

Any reasonable, well-developed idea should get three marks. Try to give the examiner three things to tick.

Notice how the first example uses three short sentences to get three marks, whereas the second develops one idea in depth.

4.   **How does Eliot make us feel sympathetic to (care about) the crying child in lines 21-22?**   (4)

> The child 'clings' to Marner's neck, which shows how desperate it is for love. It cries 'Mammy', which shows that it feels lonely and wants its mother. It feels 'bewilderment', which reminds us how confusing and scary this place must be.

You probably only need two points with evidence, so long as you clearly explain how each thing might create sympathy.

However, you will notice that the example refers to all three of the main points in these lines, in order to be safe.

5.   **In your opinion, roughly how old is the child? Give evidence to support your points.**   (5)

> Eliot calls the child 'baby', which suggests that it is very young. Also, it does not seem to know any words apart from 'Mammy', which suggests that it is not old enough to talk. However, it can walk by itself ('began to toddle about'). I therefore think that it is probably about one year old.

This question is not testing your knowledge of child development! Any answer between about six months and three years might be accepted, so long as it is supported by well-explained evidence.

You need to:

- make at least two points (2 marks);

- support your ideas with evidence (2 marks);
- say how old the child is (1 mark).

Make sure that you *explain how each quotation is relevant*.

The following answer would only get three marks, because the quotes are not explained:

> *Eliot calls the child 'baby', but it can 'toddle', so I think it is about one year old.*

6. **Based on the evidence in this passage, do you think Silas cares more about his lost gold or about the child?**   **(8)**

> The word 'gold' occurs three times in lines 4-5, so Silas must care about it a lot. He is so obsessed that at first he mistakes the child for a 'heap of gold'. However, when he realises that it is a child he stops thinking about gold completely. He 'unconsciously' makes 'hushing' sounds to calm her, which shows that he immediately cares about her happiness. Instead of sitting and thinking about his money, he 'follows her' to keep her safe. It is clear, overall, that once Silas has the child in his house he cares much more for her than his gold.

This is the sort of question you would more commonly see at 13+ than 11+.

If you can find enough points (ideally four) to argue only one side of the argument – just talking about the gold or the child – you might be able to get the marks this way.

However, you cannot really answer this question without talking about both sides: it is hard to argue that one thing is *more* important if you have not shown that the other is *less* so.

Notice the simple structure of the example:

- two points (with evidence) about the gold's importance;
- two points (with evidence) about the child;
- a conclusion, answering the question.

You will lose a mark or two if you do not clearly state which (the gold or the child) you think, overall, is more important. You should also give some sense of a reason why! You don't want to give the impression that you have chosen your answer by spinning a coin.

It is possible that a marker will expect you to say that the child is more important, because this is strongly implied by the passage. However, any reasonable examiner should also accept a well-made argument for the gold.

7. **What are your impressions of the child's personality? Explain your points carefully, giving evidence from the passage.**   **(8)**

> She is trusting, because she becomes calm and stares at Silas with a 'wide quiet gaze'. She is curious, because she 'slips' from Silas's knee and wants to 'toddle about'. She is loving, calling repeatedly for her 'Mammy'. She is brave, because she is prepared to rush into the snow to look for her mother.

You should be quite familiar with this sort of question by now. However, writing about a toddler's personality is a new challenge.

Aim to make <u>four points, with evidence for each one</u>. More points with less evidence should also be acceptable.

Three points with some extra explanation *might* be okay, but don't bank on it!

8.   **How does the author create a sense of confusion and excitement in paragraph 1 (lines 1-9)?**   (6)

> Excitement is shown by the dashes (–) in lines 4-5, as though Silas is panting. The words 'agitated' and 'violently' show the strength of his excited emotions. 'Violently' also emphasises his confusion when the gold appears to 'get larger', which must seem like magic. Eliot uses the sense of touch to show the confusing feeling of reaching for gold and finding that it is 'soft' and 'warm'.

Make sure that you talk about <u>confusion *and* excitement</u>. You should make three points, with evidence for each. The example makes four, for safety's sake, but this shouldn't be necessary.

The crucial thing is that you clearly explain <u>*how* each point conveys</u> confusion or excitement ('as though Silas is panting'; 'show the strength of his excited emotions'; 'which must seem like magic'; 'the confused feeling of … finding that it is "soft"').

9.   **Continue the story for around 10-15 lines. Do not introduce any new characters. You will be marked on the quality of your writing and the way in which you develop ideas from the passage.**   (8)

> Silas clasped the child tightly to him; for a moment he hesitated, as though in a daze. Then, with a sudden decision, he turned inside and kicked the door tight against the wind. Vaguely, as though from far away, he could hear the sound of shouting, seeming to draw nearer. He didn't greatly care. Somewhere out there was his gold, he thought for a second – but suddenly, strangely, he realised that he didn't much care about that either. 'Mammy?' mumbled the child, more a question than a cry. Silas looked down: she had taken his hand. Her hot fingertips curled tightly into his palm. The voices were near now, but Silas and the child did not move as they stared quietly into the flickering light of the fire.

Notice how this example works hard <u>to maintain the tone of the passage</u>, without needing complex vocabulary. It focuses on <u>Silas's thoughts and feelings</u>, as the passage does.

The example <u>returns to the familiar theme of the gold</u>, but explores the idea that the child has already changed Silas's feelings towards it.

Also, notice how it uses vivid images of <u>sound</u>, <u>touch</u> and <u>sight</u>. The growing relationship between Silas and the little girl is shown by the trusting way she takes his hand.

As you know by now, you will lose marks if you make more than a couple of English mistakes.